Context Clues
Reading Comprehension Book
Reading Level 2.0–3.5

—————————— • Introduction • ——————————

Welcome to the Edupress Context Clues Reading Comprehension Book. This resource is an effective tool for instruction, practice, and evaluation of student understanding of how to use context clues. It includes ideas on how to introduce context clues to students, as well as activities to help teach and practice the concept.

The reproducible activities in this book are tailored to individual, small-group, and whole-class work. They include leveled reading passages, graphic organizers, worksheets, and detailed instruction pages. These activities provide opportunities to use text, illustrations, graphics, and combinations of these elements to practice using context clues to interpret text.

The material in this book is written for readers at the 2.0–3.5 reading level. However, the activities can easily be adapted to your students' ability levels and your time frame. After introducing an activity to students, model it by working through one or two examples aloud. You may wish to also read text passages aloud to students, or they can be read silently or aloud by students. For students who need personalized help, individual and small-group activities have been included. These activities can be done alone or with a classroom aide for explicit instruction.

We know you will be pleased with the progress your students make in using context clues after using this book.

EP2366 © 2010 Demco, Inc. • 4810 Forest Run Road • Madison, WI 53704
ISBN 13: 978-1-56472-156-3

www.edupressinc.com

Table of Contents

Directions: Types of Context Clues

Whole Class/Individual

Reproduce Types of Context Clues on page 4 for each student. As a class, review the four types of context clues and their examples. Then, review a text the class has read together. Model finding the meaning of a word by looking at context clues in the text, and identify the types of context clues you have used aloud. Then select words in the text, and have students identify the types of context clues that point to their meaning. Explain that sometimes a context clue can fit into more than one category.

Individual/Small Group

Reproduce Identifying Types of Context Clues 1 and 2 on pages 5 and 6 for each student. Have students work individually or with partners to determine which type of context clue each sentence provides, writing the answer in the space next to the sentence. Have them underline the word or words in each sentence that helped them.

As an extension, challenge students to write their own sentences using the different types of context clues. Have them exchange with a partner, then underline the context clues in their partner's sentences and identify the types.

Answer Key

Identifying Types of Context Clues 1 (Page 5)

1. example
2. example
3. explanation
4. synonym
5. antonym
6. antonym
7. explanation
8. example
9. explanation
10. example

Identifying Types of Context Clues 2 (Page 6)

1. explanation
2. synonym
3. explanation
4. explanation
5. synonym
6. example
7. antonym
8. synonym
9. antonym
10. synonym

Types of Context Clues

A context clue is a hint in a sentence. If you don't know the meaning of a word, look at the other words in the sentence or paragraph. They will give you hints about the word you don't know. Here are four common types of context clues that you will find in sentences:

Synonym:

A single word that has the same meaning is somewhere in the sentence or paragraph.

EXAMPLE

The tomato was **gigantic**— I have never seen one that **large**!

Antonym:

A single word that has the opposite meaning is somewhere in the sentence or paragraph.

EXAMPLE

Mikey likes **fancy** food, but I prefer to eat **simple** meals.

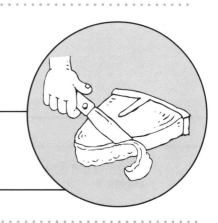

Explanation:

The word's meaning is explained with a phrase in the sentence or paragraph.

EXAMPLE

Before you cook the steak, you should **trim** the fat to **remove it** from the meat.

Example:

The word's meaning is given by one or more examples in the sentence or paragraph.

EXAMPLE

Many **flowers**, including **roses, violets, and lilacs**, have a strong scent.

Identifying Types of Context Clues 1

Directions: Write which type of context clue helped you figure out each bold word. Then, underline the context clue in the sentence.

1 _____

2 _____

3 _____

4 _____

5 _____

6 _____

7 _____

8 _____

9 _____

10 _____

1. We saw many birds at the farm. In fact, a **sparrow** flew right over our heads!

2. The carpenter's **tools** include hammers and saws.

3. If you want to know how much money your earrings are worth, take them to the jeweler. He can tell you their **value**.

4. We were **happy** to see our dog, and he was glad to see us, too.

5. The movie was **awful**, not like the wonderful one we saw last week.

6. "Take this path," Andy said. "It is **safe**, not like the dangerous one over there."

7. The **principal**, who is in charge of the teachers and students, has her own office.

8. **Vegetables**, such as beans, peas, and carrots, contain a lot of vitamins.

9. Our little brother loves his **wagon**, which has four wheels, a handle, and a place to sit.

10. Your body has many **joints**, including elbows, knees, and ankles.

Identifying Types of Context Clues 2

Name:_____

Directions: Write which type of context clue helped you figure out each bold word. Then, underline the context clue in the sentence.

1 _____

Some students got **upset** because they failed the test—in fact, Jamie started crying.

2 _____

Were the Halloween decorations **frightening**, or were they not scary at all?

3 _____

My school bus stops **frequently** because many kids get picked up and dropped off.

4 _____

My family goes to the **annual** parade, which is held every Fourth of July.

5 _____

Joey is a fast runner. Hardly anyone can beat him in a race because he is so **swift**.

6 _____

Some **languages**, such as Spanish and French, are fun to learn.

7 _____

I thought the test would be **difficult**, but it turned out to be easy.

8 _____

We heard a **faint** noise coming from the barn, but it was so quiet that we couldn't tell what it was.

9 _____

After your walk, you might feel **fatigue**, but if you rest, you will have energy again.

10 _____

Layla always **boasts** about how rich she is. Everyone is sick of hearing her brag.

Directions: Building Vocabulary

Individual

Give one copy of "In Charge" on page 8 or "Where in the World?" on page 9 to each student, along with several copies of the Vocabulary Builders Graphic Organizer on page 10. Ask students to complete the graphic organizer for each, or a set number, of the bold words in the story, using context clues and a dictionary to find the answers.

Small Group

Divide the class into pairs. Reproduce "In Charge" or "Where in the World?" along with three copies of the Vocabulary Builders Graphic Organizer for each pair. Have partners read the story aloud to each other and review the bold words. Then, have them work together to fill in the graphic organizer for three of the bold words. They can fill it in cooperatively, or have each student take one half of the organizer and write in the answers. Upon completion, the pairs should discuss and check one another's work.

Whole Class

Choose one of the stories to reproduce for each student. Then, reproduce the graphic organizer on a transparency. Have each student read a portion of the story aloud. Then, complete the graphic organizer as a class for each word. Encourage students to identify and discuss the specific context clues that lead them to the meaning of the words.

In Charge

"Julie, you are in charge," Grandma Jane **declared** in a loud voice.

Julie's brother, Nathan, was **annoyed**. He was older than Julie! Why did Grandma always put her in charge of the kids?

"It's not fair," he **grumbled**. It didn't matter if Grandma was taking them on a nature walk, a picnic, or a trip to the museum—she always asked Julie to help her.

This time, Grandma was showing the kids around the farm where she had lived when she was a little girl. There were horses and goats. The cousins were all excited to visit the farm. But Grandma had **warned** them about some bad things that could happen.

"On a farm, there are lots of ways to get hurt," she had said. "There are **dangerous** tools and barbed wire fences. And if you get too close to the biggest goat, he might try to hurt you with his horns."

Julie had listened **carefully** to every word Grandma had said. Nathan watched as she **assisted** her little cousins in the barnyard. She kept them away from the wire fence. She held their hands so they wouldn't get too close to the goat pen.

Nathan said to himself, "Julie thinks she's so great at watching little kids. I could take care of them, too." Suddenly, Nathan had an idea. He ran up to Julie. "Hey," he said to her.

"I can watch one of the little cousins."

Julie looked at him **doubtfully**. "Do you remember all the things that Grandma said?" she asked with a frown.

"Of course," Nathan said. He took his little cousin's hand. He'd show Grandma and Julie that they could **trust** him. He wouldn't let them down.

When they got to the **corral** where the horses lived, Nathan's mouth fell open in **amazement**. He'd never seen such beautiful animals! He dropped his cousin's hand and climbed on the fence to get a better look. There were black, brown, and white horses. Their **gorgeous** manes flew in the wind as they ran around the corral. They were beautiful. Nathan couldn't take his eyes off them.

Suddenly, Nathan heard a scream. He turned around and saw everyone running toward the pen where the goats were kept. But the goats weren't alone in the pen. Nathan was **horrified** to see his little cousin in the pen with them. He had stopped paying **attention** for one second. That was long enough for him to get into trouble.

Nathan ran toward the goats' pen. He climbed over the fence and grabbed his little cousin just before the biggest goat **charged** straight at them. They got out of the way just in time!

Where in the World?

When you eat a yummy fruit salad, you are **enjoying** food that farmers have grown. It takes months for most fruits to grow. The people who grow these foods spend a lot of time and **energy** taking care of their trees and plants. They take great pride in their work.

Some farmers live where the **weather** is always sunny. Some farms get just the right amount of rain. Other farmers must **provide** water so that the fruits will grow. All farmers have to get **rid** of the weeds that grow in the fields. Farmers **often** spend all day and even some nights working in the fields. There are not many days when they don't work hard all day.

It might seem like a lot of **labor** for a few baskets of apples or cherries. But millions of people **depend** on farmers' hard work to grow food. Without farmers, stores would not be stocked with many of the foods you eat. The next time that you are at the store, **pause** for a moment. Look at how many people are buying fruit. Notice how many different and colorful fruits you can see. They all look fresh and **delicious**. Each time

you visit the store, you will see bins full of bananas, oranges, and berries. There are many **varieties** of fruits. It is hard to count all the kinds you see at the store. Some of these foods come from faraway places. Many plants grow best in other **countries**—not in the United States. When you buy a piece of fruit, it will have a sticker on it. This sticker will tell you if the fruit was grown in a different country.

The next time you make fruit salad, try this activity. On a world map, make a mark where each fruit came from. Then **measure** how many miles the fruit traveled to get to your plate. You might be surprised. Add up all the miles. Is it more than one **thousand**? That is a long way! Many people worked very hard to grow those fruits. Others worked hard to pick them and load them onto trucks. The drivers worked hard to get them to the store. If these people worked slowly, the fruit would **rot** before anyone got to eat it. However, the fruit is still fresh by the time it gets to the store. Fresh fruit and vegetables are **healthy**. They are good for you. They taste better, too.

Name:_____

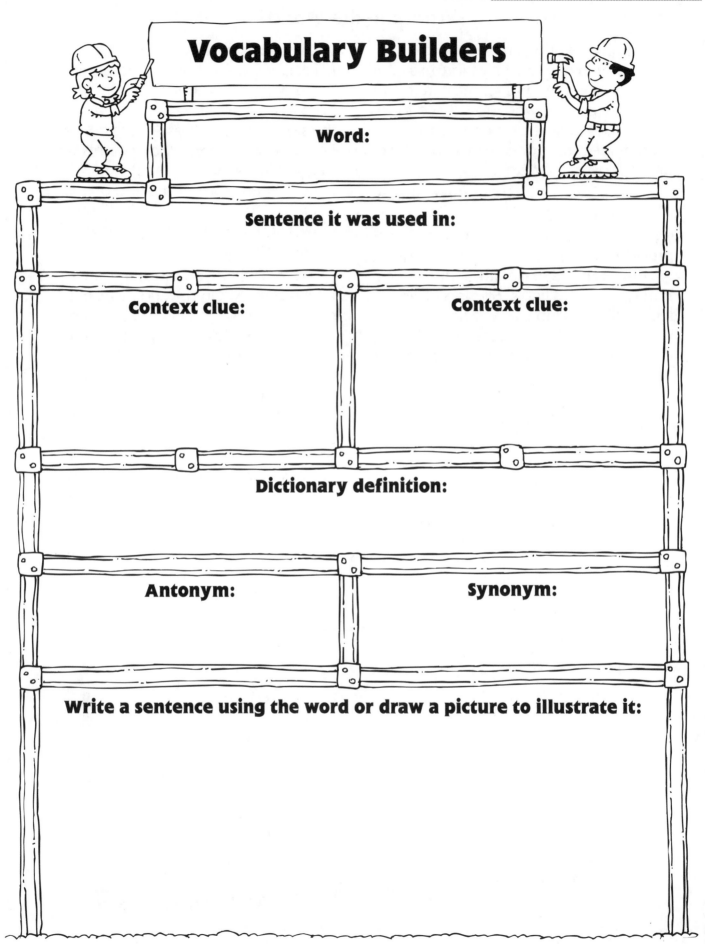

Vocabulary Builders

Word:

Sentence it was used in:

Context clue: **Context clue:**

Dictionary definition:

Antonym: **Synonym:**

Write a sentence using the word or draw a picture to illustrate it:

Directions: Silly Sentences

Individual ●

Reproduce a Silly Sentences worksheet on page 12 or 13 for each student. Tell students to find and circle the word that doesn't fit in the context of each sentence and write an appropriate word underneath. Discuss the activity as a class, and explain that there might be more than one word that can replace the incorrect word.

Small Group ● ●

Make multiple copies of the Silly Sentence Cards on page 14, cut them apart, and give each student five cards. Ask students to write a sentence on each card. Four of the sentences should make sense, and the fifth should be a silly sentence with a word that doesn't fit. Divide the class into groups of five. In each group, have students take turns handing out their cards. Each student should read one aloud. The team should then decide which sentence contains a word that doesn't fit the context. The person holding that card is then challenged to state a word that fits correctly in the sentence.

For pairs of students, make multiple copies of the Silly Sentence Cards, cut them apart, and split them between the two students. Ask them to write their own silly sentences, using at least one word that does not fit in the context of each sentence. Have each student trade with a partner, and have the partner circle clues in each sentence that show which word is not contextually correct.

Whole Class ● ● ●

Use the Silly Sentence Cards to write several correct sentences and several that contain a word that does not fit the context. Put the cards in a bag. Divide the class into two teams, and have Team One pick a card from the bag and read the sentence out loud to Team Two. Team Two must then determine if the sentence is "silly" or "correct." If the team is right, they earn a point. If they can replace an incorrect word with a context-correct word, they earn another point. Play then passes to the other team and can continue until a desired point level is reached or until all sentences are used.

Answer Key (suggested answers)

Silly Sentences 1 (Page 12)

1. picture; window
2. pillow; white/black
3. rake; light
4. bicycling; hopping
5. cracker; horse
6. eating; running
7. cute; cold
8. banana; cabin/house
9. shape; color
10. wheelbarrow; year

Silly Sentences 2 (Page 13)

1. boss; animal
2. washed; asked
3. lazy; tall/large
4. fort; school
5. horse; butterfly
6. magazine; dinner
7. medium; first
8. laughed; rained
9. roads; nights
10. hear; see

Silly Sentences 1

Directions: Circle the word that doesn't belong in each sentence. Write the correct word below the sentence.

1 Andy and Molly looked out the picture to see if Mom was home from work yet.

2 My new puppy, who we named Otis, is brown and has pillow spots.

3 Before electricity, people used lanterns to rake up their houses at night.

4 In the country of Australia, you can see kangaroos bicycling along the road.

5 The man put the saddle on his cracker and rode off into the sunset.

6 Runners should have a snack before a race, or they will get tired from eating around the track.

7 When water gets very cute, it becomes a solid and is called ice.

8 This book is about a family who lives in a very small banana that is made of logs.

9 I love Anna's new jacket because it is purple, my favorite shape.

10 My littlest brother did not know that there are 365 days in a wheelbarrow.

Silly Sentences 2

Directions: Circle the word that doesn't belong in each sentence. Write the correct word below the sentence.

1 The white-tailed deer is the state boss of Wisconsin.

2 Mom washed the kids, "Who will take the books back to the library?"

3 Oak trees grow very lazy, but it takes many years for them to get that big.

4 If you don't run to the bus stop, you will miss the bus and be late to fort.

5 The Monarch horse is beautiful because of its black and orange wings.

6 Peter set the dining room table for magazine, but he forgot the salt and pepper in the kitchen.

7 George Washington was the medium president of the United States.

8 It laughed so hard that the river flooded the town.

9 In the winter, the days are shorter, and the roads are longer.

10 Aunt Maria put the flowers in a vase and set them on the table, so now everyone can hear them.

13

Silly Sentence Cards

Directions: Silly Stories

Individual

Reproduce "A Helping Hand" on page 16 and "A New Friend" on page 17 for each student. Use the first to model using context clues to figure out the missing words. Talk aloud, and model your thinking process as you read and identify the context clues. Then, have students read the second story and fill in the blanks. Ask them to underline the context clues that helped them guess the missing words. Discuss the activity as a class.

Small Group

Divide the class into pairs. On copies of "A Helping Hand" and "A New Friend," write the part of speech for each missing word under the blank. Then, give each student a copy of one of the labeled stories. Be sure to give each partner a different story. Then, without letting his or her partner see the story, one student should ask for a word that matches the part of speech for each blank in the story. After the words are all filled in, the other partner can read the silly version aloud. After the silly story is read, have the partners discuss which words would fit in the blanks to make the story make sense. Then, have students switch roles with the other story. Ask for volunteers to share their silly stories with the class.

Whole Class

Divide the class into two teams. Have each student write a sentence with a missing word. Tell students to include context clues in their sentences to allow others to guess the missing word. Have the first team read a sentence aloud or write it on the board, and challenge the other team to come up with the missing word. Give a point for each correct word. Play then passes to the other team and can continue until a desired point level is reached or all sentences are used.

Answer Key

"A Helping Hand" (Page 16)

- bus
- studied
- park
- read
- house/windows
- calling/shouting
- friends
- door
- help
- newspapers
- catch

"A New Friend" (Page 17)

- puppy
- teach
- work
- food
- water
- sleep
- puppy
- walks
- neck
- walk
- nap
- food
- eats
- good
- plate

A Helping Hand

"It's finally the weekend!" Jordan exclaimed. He stepped off the school _____ and watched it drive away. It had been a long, hard week. He'd _____ hard for three tests. There had been no time to break in his new baseball mitt.

Jordan raced down the sidewalk toward home. He needed to hurry. Andrew and Yasmine were waiting for him. They were going to the _____ to play catch.

As he ran, Jordan noticed that his neighbor, Mrs. Duncan, hadn't picked up today's newspaper from the sidewalk.

"That's weird," he thought. Mrs. Duncan loved reading the sports section of the paper. On warm days, she would sit on her front porch swing and _____ every word. Jordan stopped and looked at the old woman's _____. The shades were down, which was strange, too. As he stood on the sidewalk, he saw yesterday's newspaper on the porch steps. He heard Andrew and Yasmine down the street. They were _____ his name.

Jordan wanted to go play catch with his _____. He also wanted to see if Mrs. Duncan was okay. He was worried that she might be sick.

Finally, he called to the other kids, "Go on without me. I have to check on something." Andrew and Yasmine raced off toward the park. Jordan sighed. Then he ran to his house and asked his dad to help check on Mrs. Duncan.

It took the old woman a long time to answer the _____. As she opened it, Jordan could see the relief on her face.

"Thank goodness you're here," she said. "I twisted my ankle and haven't been able to move very much. I didn't want to bother anyone, but I sure could use some _____."

Jordan's dad went home to get the car to drive Mrs. Duncan to the doctor. Jordan stayed with Mrs. Duncan. He found a cane she could use to help her walk. Then he went outside and brought her the _____ on the sidewalk. By the time his dad came back, Jordan and Mrs. Duncan were looking at the sports pages. They were discussing the baseball team's chances of making it to the World Series this year.

After they had driven her to the doctor and back home, Mrs. Duncan was comfortable and happy. Andrew promised he'd stop in tomorrow and chat about baseball. He had missed his chance to play _____, but he didn't mind. He was just glad Mrs. Duncan was okay.

A New Friend

Getting a new dog is exciting. A young _____ is a lot of fun. If your family is getting a dog, there are many things to look forward to. You can help choose the dog's name. You will be able to play with it. You can _____ it tricks.

Owning a puppy is fun, but it also is a lot of _____. You have to walk the dog. You have to clean up after it. You have to train it. You have to make sure it has _____ to eat and fresh _____ to drink.

When you first bring your puppy home, it might cry and whine at night. It probably misses its mother. If you are patient at bedtime, the dog will soon learn to go to _____ on its own. A cozy, warm, clean bed will help it relax.

You also need to provide a safe place for the _____ to play. Make sure you keep small objects off the floor. Puppies love to chew on things. You do not want the dog to get something stuck in its throat.

You should take your puppy for _____. You have to keep it on a leash, even if it does not like it. It might not like the way the collar feels around its _____. Your puppy might leap up and try to bite at the leash while you are training it. Try to be patient.

After you take your puppy for a _____, it will be very tired and will want a nap. Puppies _____ a lot. Napping helps them grow and keeps them healthy.

Sometimes, your puppy will be so hungry that it will gobble its _____. Other times, it might be too busy playing to remember to eat. You have to make sure your puppy _____ the right amount of food.

It's important to give your puppy the right kind of food, too. Letting it eat the same food you eat is not a _____ idea. Humans and dogs need different kinds of food. Even if your dog is begging, you should not give it food from your _____.

After you have taken care of all your dog's needs, it's time to play. This will be your puppy's favorite part of the day!

Directions: What Is the Meaning of This?

Individual

Reproduce "The Lesson" on page 19 and "Eggs Come in All Sizes" on page 21 and their matching vocabulary worksheets on pages 20 and 22 for each student. Have students read one story, circling the words throughout that give clues to the meanings of the unfamiliar bold words. They can then use the vocabulary worksheet to write down what they believe each word means. Share the correct definitions with the class and ask how many students got them right.

Before students read the next story, ask them to fill in any definitions on the list they think they already know. After they read the story, ask them to assess these definitions and to write definitions for the other words. When all students have finished, ask students to share their definitions. How many did they already know? How many did they figure out from reading the story?

Small Group

Divide students into pairs. Reproduce either "The Lesson" or "Eggs Come in All Sizes" along with two matching vocabulary worksheets for each pair. After they read the story aloud together, have students individually write down what they think each bold word means. When they are finished, have partners exchange their lists, then look up the words in dictionaries. They should circle the correct definitions on their partners' lists and compare their answers afterward.

Whole Class

Reproduce one of the stories along with its matching vocabulary worksheet for each student. Have each student read the story and write definitions for the words on the list. When students are finished, read the correct definitions aloud, asking students to circle the words they got correct. When all the definitions are read, collect the lists and graph on the board how many students got one, two, three, etc., correct. Then discuss the results. Were the words most students got correct ones they were already familiar with?

The Lesson

Mark was so excited he could barely sit still. Today he was going to have his very first violin lesson! He couldn't wait to learn to play as well as his big sister. Sherry always **performed** when the family had a party. Everyone loved to hear her play the violin.

Mark knew Sherry worked hard. She practiced each song **multiple** times. When she first began to learn a song, the music sounded **dreadful**. But the more she practiced, the better the song sounded.

Sherry spent an hour each night practicing. Sometimes she practiced longer. Mark wondered if he would have to practice that much. He would miss his favorite television shows. Maybe he wouldn't have time to play with his friends.

After his lesson, Mark told Sherry, "Playing isn't as easy as I had hoped it would be. The teacher gave me some practice scales to work on this week. She said that if I worked hard, I would **improve** quickly. I want to get better, so I'm going to practice right now!"

Mark did **intend** to practice, but just then, his friend Alex came over. The boys decided to go to the skate park instead. They **remained** there until dinnertime. Mark forgot about practicing until he heard Sherry playing her violin. She sounded so good that he felt **embarrassed** to practice with the whole family listening. He was afraid he would sound terrible.

The next day, Mark and Sherry practiced for an hour after school. Sherry **demonstrated** how to hold the bow and how to tune the strings. Mark was glad she showed him how.

"I really have two violin teachers," he **announced** to his mom and dad at dinner.

His second lesson was great. The teacher couldn't believe how good he sounded.

"You must have **concentrated** on practicing this week," Ms. Taylor said. "I can tell you spent more time on it."

After that, Mark felt like he could relax a little. Maybe he didn't need to practice so much. There were so many other fun things to do, like play video games or go to the swimming pool.

Mark hardly practiced at all the next week —and it showed at his lesson. The teacher seemed **disappointed** in him. Mark was disappointed in himself, too.

"I should have practiced more," he told Sherry later. "Everyone says that if I want to improve, I have to be **dedicated**. I have to practice nearly every day, and I have to keep **attending** lessons. That's my plan from now on!"

Vocabulary for "The Lesson"

demonstrated

announced

concentrated

disappointed

dedicated

attending

performed

multiple

dreadful

improve

intend

remained

embarrassed

Eggs Come in All Sizes

Gaze out your window. Do you see any birds? If you live in the city, you might see pigeons. If you **reside** in the country, you might see robins or bluebirds.

Birds **select** different places to live, just as people do. Some birds live near the ocean, and some make their homes in forests. They **construct** homes, just as people do. Some birds build nests in trees, and some choose to live in holes in trees.

But all birds have one thing in common: they lay eggs. Chicken eggs are white or brown, and they are about as big as a child's hand. Some birds lay eggs that are much bigger than that. But some lay eggs that are tiny in **comparison** to chicken eggs.

The ostrich is a huge bird. It is as tall as an adult. So it is not **surprising** that an ostrich egg is **extremely** large. In fact, the egg is about the size of an adult chicken!

A hummingbird is a tiny bird. It is only about three inches long—that is about the size of an adult's thumb. How big do you think a hummingbird's egg is? If you guessed that it is tiny, your guess would be **accurate**. A hummingbird's egg is about as big as your fingernail.

Many of the birds that you see outside lay eggs that are smaller than a chicken's egg. Some are colored.

For example, a robin's egg is light blue. Other birds lay eggs that are dotted with brown and white.

If you see a nest that has eggs in it, you should not **disturb** it. The mother bird is somewhere nearby. She will **return** soon because she must sit on the eggs most of the time. This keeps the eggs warm and helps the baby birds **develop**. They need the warmth to grow.

Do you think the mother bird gets tired of sitting on those eggs? Well, she needs to get some rest while she can! When the little birds hatch from the eggs, they will **require** lots of food. They need to eat a lot to be healthy. It is the mother bird's job to feed them. She will spend most of her days flying back and forth from the nest to the ground. She will find bugs and seeds and feed them to the baby birds.

Soon, the baby birds will have grown to twice their **original** size. It is hard to believe that they once fit into a little egg.

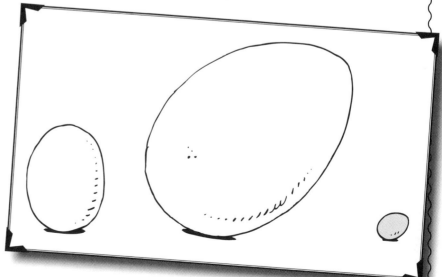

Vocabulary for "Eggs Come in All Sizes"

accurate _____

disturb _____

return _____

develop _____

require _____

original _____

gaze _____

reside _____

select _____

construct _____

comparison _____

surprising _____

extremely _____

Directions: Made-Up Words

Individual ●

Reproduce "A Birthday Tweet" on page 24 or "The Art of Painting" on page 25 for each student. Ask students to read the story and circle the words they think are made up. On another sheet of paper, have them write each suspect word, then a real word that they think might take its place. Then, have them highlight or underline the context clues in the story that helped them figure out the real words. As a class, discuss the made-up words and what they might mean.

Small Group ● ●

Have students write their own stories, then go through and replace several real words with made-up ones. Ask them to exchange their stories with a partner. Have partners read the new stories, circle the words they think are made up, and replace them with appropriate words. Then, have students discuss with their partners why they chose these new words.

Whole Class

Using the answer key below, make a list on the board, out of order, of words that can replace the made-up words in the stories. Then, reproduce the story on a transparency. Read the story aloud to the class. As you read, ask students to raise their hands or stand up if they hear a word they think is made up. Circle the words on the transparency as students identify them. After you've finished reading the story, go through the story and read the sentences with made-up words in them. Challenge students to be the first to find a word from the list on the board to replace the made-up word and shout it out. Ask the other students if they agree. Write the correct word on the transparency.

Answer Key (suggested answers)

"A Birthday Tweet" (Page 24)

jembled = jumped
followy = finally
timents = minutes
wollow = now
brossel = watch
masserly = snapping
Fortu = Open
merring = talking
yasert = present
derks = birds
rerdas = words
markelly = quickly
nurst = into
weally = pretty
gared = said
umpers = twins

"The Art of Painting" (Page 25)

frews = flowers
martus = artist
mickel = choose/pick
furb = paint
lillios = colors
helder = black
jeaker = darker
ghule = yellow
minnel = small
kider = paper
nowes = brushes
shelpers = painters/artists
drog = paint
crique = paint
gorn = wall

A Birthday Tweet

Maria and Marcus jembled out of the car as soon as Mom turned it off. They raced each other to the pet shop door. They had waited so long for this day, and now it was follow here!

Mom laughed at them. "The store does not open until 10 o'clock," she said. "We will have to wait for three timents. Then, Mr. Swanson will unlock the door."

The twins made faces at each other.

"Three minutes?" Marcus wailed. "But I want to pick out our birds right wollow!"

"Three minutes is not a very long time," Maria pointed out. She looked at the brossel on her wrist. "In fact, now it's only two minutes to 10 o'clock."

The twins passed the next two minutes by peering into the window of the pet shop. They could see hamster cages. They could see fish tanks filled with colorful fish. They even saw a big tank that had a masserly turtle in it. But they could not see to the back of the store where the birds were kept.

Finally, they saw Mr. Swanson at the door. He smiled at them as he turned the "Closed" sign around. Now the sign read, "Fortu."

The minute Mr. Swanson unlocked the door, the twins rushed inside.

"Good morning," Mr. Swanson called to them as they hurried past him toward the back room. Their mother followed more slowly. The twins heard her merring to Mr. Swanson.

"Today is the day," she told the pet shop owner. "They are nine years old. They each get to choose a bird. That is their birthday yasert."

Marcus went straight to the cage that held the parrots. The bright, colorful derks looked at him. Some spoke real rerdas because they had been trained to talk. Some just made bird noises.

Maria looked at the tiny finches. These little birds flew very markelly from their perches to their nests. They were so fast! As they flew, they made little peeping noises. Maria loved how cute their orange beaks looked.

Then Marcus said, "Oh, Maria, look!"

Maria came over to the cage. She looked nurst it. There were two birds. One was yellow. One was green. They were sitting close together on a perch. They looked at the twins.

"What kind of birds are these?" Maria asked.

Mr. Swanson answered, "People call them lovebirds. They are really parakeets."

"They are such weally colors," Maria said.

"They look friendly," Marcus gared.

"They are perfect!" the umpers said together.

The Art of Painting

Do you know anyone who paints beautiful pictures? Many people make paintings for fun. It is a good hobby. You can paint pictures of anything you like. Some people like to paint frews and trees. Some paint pictures of people. Some artists make pictures that don't look like anything at all. They just make shapes or patterns with colors.

If you are going to be a martus, you will need some supplies. First, you must decide what kind of paint to use. There are several kinds of paints to mickel from. Some paints are made from water. Some are made from oil. Water paints are easy to clean up, but some people choose oil because they like the way the furb looks.

Both kinds of paint come in many lillios. There are hundreds of shades of each color, but you don't have to buy many tubes of paint. You can mix colors very easily. If you buy a big tube of helder paint and another big tube of white paint, you can make light and dark shades of other colors.

Red is a good color to make lighter or jeaker. If you add black to it, it becomes darker, the color of bricks. If you add white to it, it turns pink. You can make many other shades by adding more or less black or white to the red paint. You can also do this with ghule paint to make a bright sun.

Before you begin, you will need to buy brushes. Make sure you get at least one big brush and one tiny brush. The big brush will come in handy when you want to cover a lot of your paper with paint. The minnel brush will help you make small details in your painting. A medium-sized brush is useful, too.

People usually paint on white paper. You can buy special paper for your paints. You can also practice on regular writing kider.

You now have paper, paints, and nowes. You are ready to paint, as long as you have an idea for a picture. Some artists look around the house or out the window. They see something they would like to paint. Other shelpers use photographs for ideas. Some ask people to sit or stand still while they drog them.

Once your painting is finished, put it in a safe place to dry. Clean up any crique you have spilled. Wash your brushes, and put them away until next time. When your painting is dry, hang it on the gorn. You are an artist!

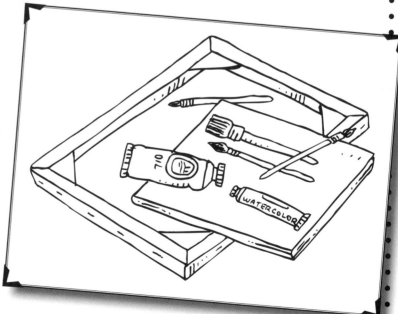

Directions: Multiple-Meaning Words

Individual

Reproduce Multiple-Meaning Words 1 and 2 on pages 27 and 28 for each student. Have students read the sentence groups and circle the letters of the two sentences that use the word in the same way. Then, have students choose one of the words and illustrate both of its meanings on the side of the page.

Also, reproduce Homonym Multiple Choice on page 30 for each student. Explain that homonyms are words that sound the same but are spelled differently and have different meanings. Have students circle the correct word for each sentence.

As an extension, have students use the Multiple-Meaning Word Cards on page 29 to write two sentences, one for each meaning of the word. Or, challenge them to write sentences that use both meanings of each word in the same sentence.

Small Group ● ●

Reproduce the Multiple-Meaning Word Cards for each student. Have each student choose five words from the list and write a one-page story using them. Divide students into groups of three or four, and have them read their stories aloud. Ask them to discuss how they got the ideas for their stories

(this develops the skills of using prior knowledge and connecting text to self). Ask them to discover if others in their group chose the same words but used them with their different meanings.

Whole Class ● ● ●

Divide the class into two teams. Reproduce the Multiple-Meaning Word Cards and separate them into two groups. Give each team one group of words. Have each team write a sentence on a strip of paper for each of their words. Have the first team read a sentence out loud. The other team then states the multiple-meaning word and the definition of that word. If they are correct, they get a point. Play passes to the other team. Play until all words have been used. A bonus round can be done by repeating the multiple-meaning words and having teams shout out a second meaning for the word, with the first team to get the answer receiving the point.

Or, divide the class into two teams. Call out one of the multiple-meaning words. Have each student secretly draw the meaning of the word you've called out. At the end of a time limit, have teams compare papers. Count how many students on each team had similar drawings.

Answer Key

Multiple-Meaning Words 1 (Page 27)		Multiple-Meaning Words 2 (Page 28)	Homonym Multiple Choice (Page 30)	
1. a, c		1. a, c	1. b	7. b
2. a, c		2. b, c	2. a	8. b
3. b, c		3. a, c	3. a	9. a
4. b, c		4. b, c	4. b	10. a
			5. a	11. b
			6. a	12. b

h set, circle the two sentences that use the same meaning of the bold
ose one of the sets of words and illustrate its two different meanings.

| | **Meaning 1** |

annot see the board unless she
ing her **glasses**.

b When we do the dishes after dinner, we
wash the **glasses** first, then the plates.

c The eye doctor checks your vision
and makes sure your **glasses**
fit properly.

2

a It is four **blocks** from my house
to school.

b My little brother likes to play
with **blocks**.

c Marty is not allowed to cross the street
—he has to stay on his own **block**.

Meaning 2

3

a The cat likes to **spring** across the room
to chase her toys.

b In **spring**, we take walks through the
park and look at the flowers.

c After the long winter, we look forward
to enjoying **spring** weather.

4

a Morgan had **tears** in his eyes after he
saw what had happened.

b Morgan was upset because there were
several **tears** in his new jacket.

c Morgan's aunt will sew up the **tears**,
and the jacket will be as good as new.

Multiple-Meaning Words 2

Name:_____

Directions: In each set, circle the two sentences that use the same meaning of the bold word. Then, choose one of the sets of words and illustrate its two different meanings.

1

(a) The magician pulled a **dove** from out of his hat and let it fly away.

(b) Brianna **dove** off the high board at swimming lessons today.

(c) There is a **dove** that sits in the tree outside and coos.

2

(a) "Be **patient**," Mom said. "You will get your turn on the swings soon."

(b) The doctor checked the **patient** to see if he had a fever.

(c) When you are a **patient** in the hospital, you should get lots of rest.

3

(a) Ryan's older sister ran three times around the **track**.

(b) I saw a **track** in the sand that looked like a dog had been there.

(c) The **track** at school is open for runners of all ages.

4

(a) We sat in the traffic jam for a long time, listening to people honk their **horns**.

(b) Billy goats often have long **horns**.

(c) "Do deer have **horns** or antlers?" Jesse asked his mom.

Meaning 1

Meaning 2

Multiple-Meaning Word Cards

match	**trip**	**spy**
kind	**swing**	**lock**
dust	**stuff**	**save**
ring	**space**	**dust**
plant	**pack**	**skate**
sink	**spell**	**dress**
fan	**rose**	**pound**

Homonym Multiple Choice

Name:_____

Directions: Choose the word that best fits each blank in the sentences below.

 1 Sarah didn't mean to _____ her grandmother's favorite vase.

   a) brake   b) break

 2 The principal _____ for James and Cassie because they were in trouble.

   a) sent   b) cent

 3 A horse's _____ can be many different colors, including red, black, brown, or white.

   a) mane   b) main

4 Nicky _____ the ball too hard, and it flew right over Angie's head.

   a) through   b) threw

 5 Little kids get _____ staying inside all day, so you should take them out to play.

   a) bored   b) board

 6 Being a _____ student at school is tough, especially if you are shy.

   a) new   b) knew

 7 "Will you _____ your little brother another glass of milk?" Grandma asked.

   a) poor   b) pour

 8 Some people do not eat _____, just vegetables, fruit, cheese and milk.

   a) meet   b) meat

 9 "Who _____ what the capital of Texas is?" Ms. Evans asked.

   a) knows   b) nose

 10 When the moon is full, it looks like a _____ circle.

   a) whole   b) hole

 11 Grandpa said to Aaron, "I can't believe how tall you have _____!"

   a) groan   b) grown

12 We saw a _____ of cows that were black and white.

   a) heard   b) herd

Directions: Nonsense Words

Individual

Reproduce the Nonsense Word Cards on page 32 for each student. Ask each student to come up with a definition for each word, then to use it in a sentence. On separate sheets of paper, have students illustrate the definitions for three words. Students will draw on their prior knowledge, vocabulary, and knowledge of word origins to come up with definitions. Discuss with them how they chose certain definitions for words.

Small Group

Have students exchange one or two of their drawings from the Individual activity with a partner (make sure they've written the nonsense word at the top). Have partners write down what they think the meaning of the nonsense word is based on the drawing. Have partners reveal, compare, and discuss the made-up definitions. Were they correct in their guesses? What things in the drawings made them guess the definitions that they did? Alternatively, have students trade their sentences with partners. Have partners try to guess the meanings of the words using context clues from the sentences. If their definitions were similar, ask them to discuss what made them think of that meaning. Did the word look like another word? Did it sound like another word? If the partners' definitions weren't similar, did they choose to use the words in the same manner (i.e., nouns, verbs, etc.)?

Whole Class

Reproduce the Nonsense Word Cards and cut them apart. Put the words in a bag. Divide the class into two teams. Have one student from each team draw a card. They each have 30 seconds to write a sentence using their nonsense words on the board. When the time is up, their team must guess the meaning of the word using context clues from their sentence. If the team is correct, they earn a point. If the team is stumped, they can guess if the word is being used as a noun, verb, etc., for a half point. The team with the most points at the end wins.

Nonsense Word Cards

margle	gumbun
mugdog	freapy
frownbuster	hapsilly
mooper	tridog
purpquacker	seafest
tribless	boomdown
kittest	firerun
wigfittle	nosemoo
mednoodle	werdnit
rosekettle	probam
chindex	underhouse

Directions: What's the Word?

Reproduce What's the Word? 1 and 2 on pages 34 and 35 for each student. Have students use context clues to fill in the missing words. Ask them to underline the clues in each sentence that led them to the correct answer. When all students are finished, discuss the answers as a class. Some sentences might have more than one correct word. Discuss the reasons students chose the words they did.

Small Group ●●

Divide students into pairs. Ask them each to write five sentences with missing words. (They might find it easier to write complete sentences, then choose a word that is surrounded by context clues and remove that word.) Then, have students exchange papers with their partners and fill in the missing words. Students can then discuss the results with their partners.

Whole Class ●●●

Reproduce the What's the Word? pages on transparencies. Divide the class into two teams. Show one sentence at a time and ask one member from each team to call out a word that fits in the blank as quickly as they can. Teams are awarded a point each time a member calls out a correct answer first.

Answer Key (suggested answers)

What's the Word? 1 (Page 34)	What's the Word? 2 (Page 35)
1. bell	1. shoes
2. night	2. lazy/tired
3. lights/power	3. strings
4. people	4. weeds
5. homework	5. hear
6. years	6. build/make
7. tallest	7. see/watch
8. math	8. country
9. mirror	9. don't
10. car	10. colors
11. glasses	11. remember
12. beach	

Name:_____

Directions: Use context clues to fill in the missing word in each sentence.

1 By the time the second school _____ rings, we are supposed to be in our seats.

2 Butterflies are active during the day, but moths usually come out at _____ .

3 During the thunderstorm, the _____ went out, and we had to use flashlights to see.

4 The most popular topping for pizza is sausage, but many _____ like mushrooms, too.

5 "How many of you finished your _____ last night?" Ms. Dylan asked the class.

6 If you go to a museum, you can see objects that are hundreds of _____ old, but you cannot touch them.

7 Eric and Martin are quite tall, but Greg is the _____ boy in the whole class.

8 My favorite subject in school is reading, but I like _____ too, because addition is easy for me.

9 I looked in the _____ to make sure my face was clean.

10 My dad took the _____ to the mechanic because it was not running right.

11 "Did anyone see where I left my _____ ?" Grandpa asked. "I want to read the paper, and I can't do it without them."

12 We enjoyed our trip to the _____ because it was fun to see the surfers riding on the waves.

ntext clues to fill in the missing word in each sentence.

1 Marcus needs new ▢▢▢ for gym class, so his aunt is taking him to the Fast Foot Shop.

2 The lawn needs to be mowed, but Anna is feeling too ▢▢▢ to do it —she would rather just watch television.

3 A guitar has six strings, but a bass guitar has two fewer than that. Simon has broken all four ▢▢▢ on his bass this week.

4 The best part about growing a garden is picking the good, ripe vegetables. The worst part is pulling up all the ▢▢▢ that grow in the garden, too!

5 "Hello," Devin said into the phone. "Hello, hello—can you ▢▢▢ me?"

6 People use wood to ▢▢▢ furniture and houses.

7 This year, the school play will be Jack and the Beanstalk. Our families will come to ▢▢▢ it.

8 Canada is a ▢▢▢ that is north of the United States of America.

9 Kevin and Mason like the same music, but they ▢▢▢ like the same television shows.

10 The ▢▢▢ of the rainbow are red, orange, yellow, green, blue, indigo, and violet.

11 "Did you ▢▢▢ to take the dog for a walk today, or did you forget again?" Dad asked.

Directions: Using Antonyms and Synonyms as Context Clues

Individual ⬤

Discuss synonyms and antonyms with the class. Reproduce Antonyms and Synonyms Context Clues 1 and 2 on pages 37 and 38 for each student. Have students read the sentences and then circle the antonym or synonym that gives the context clue for the definition of the bold word. Have them write an "S" or an "A" above to show whether it is a synonym or antonym. Discuss the answers as a class.

Small Group ⬤⬤

Divide students into pairs. Reproduce Synonym/Antonym Cards 1 and 2 on pages 39 and 40 for each pair and cut them apart. Put the cards in a bag, and have each student pull a card out of the bag. Students can then use the word to write a sentence that gives context clues to its meaning through a synonym or antonym (allow them to use a dictionary or thesaurus if they need help). Rotate through groups to make sure students are using their words correctly. Have them underline their words in their sentences and exchange with partners. Partners try to figure out the meaning of the underlined word. If they get it right, they earn a point. Play continues until the set time is up or the pairs use all the words.

Whole Class ⬤⬤⬤

Reproduce two sets of Synonym/Antonym Cards 1 and 2. Divide the class into two teams. Give each team member a card. Have students use the word to write a sentence that gives context clues to its meaning through a synonym or antonym. Students take turns stating their words and reading their sentences to their teammates. Teammates guess the meaning of the word. If they get it right, the team gets a point. Bonus points can be earned if the students correctly identify the synonym or antonym that provides the context clue for each word. The team with the most points at the end wins the game.

Answer Key

Antonyms and Synonyms Context Clues 1 (Page 37)

1. antonym, safe
2. antonym, common
3. synonym, loud
4. antonym, thin
5. antonym, full
6. synonym, caught
7. antonym, stop
8. synonym, smart
9. antonym, sharp
10. antonym, here
11. antonym, clean
12. antonym, lazy

Antonyms and Synonyms Context Clues 2 (Page 38)

1. synonym, wrecked
2. synonym, lucky
3. synonym, smart
4. antonym, clean
5. antonym, offered
6. synonym, weak
7. synonym, rude
8. synonym, fancy
9. antonym, slowly
10. antonym, wild
11. antonym, friends
12. synonym, happy

the antonym or synonym that helps you understand the meaning of the
"S" or an "A" to show if it is an antonym or a synonym for the bold word.

1 s **dangerous** to cross the street without looking, so to stay safe, look both ways.

2 Gray rocks are common, but red rocks are **rare**. If you find a red rock, you are lucky.

3 "It is so loud in here," Rachel complained. "Why is everyone being so **noisy**?"

4 Joey likes to wear **bulky** sweaters, but thin ones fit better under his coat.

5 I was **starving** before dinner, but now I am so full that I don't want to eat any more.

6 Have you ever caught fireflies before? We have **captured** them in a jar.

7 I will **continue** to read my book, but Rico will stop reading his.

8 Derrick is very smart. People go to him with their problems because he is **wise**.

9 You can't chop wood with a **dull** ax. You must make it sharp first.

10 The teacher will mark you as **absent** if you are not here when she takes attendance.

11 Our mother said our bedroom was **filthy**. We spent all morning making it clean.

12 If you don't get enough sleep, you will feel lazy instead of **energetic**.

Antonyms and Synonyms
Context Clues 2

Name:_____

Directions: Circle the antonym or synonym that helps you understand the meaning of the bold word. Write an "S" or an "A" to show if it is an antonym or a synonym for the bold word.

1   "Who wrecked Jamie's sand castle?" Mom asked. "Whoever **destroyed** it will be in trouble."

2   We are **fortunate** to have a swimming pool. Everyone tells us how lucky we are.

3   Chimps are very **intelligent**—in fact, they are smart enough to learn all kinds of tricks.

4   Before my parents let me have friends over, they make sure my room is clean. No one wants to spend time in an **untidy** room.

5   Haley offered Franco a glass of water, but he **refused** it because he wasn't thirsty.

6   Kittens are weak when they are first born. They are so **feeble** that they can't even stand up.

7   It is **impolite** to leave without saying goodbye. If you don't want to be rude, you should say goodbye.

8   Kari thought her mother looked **elegant** when she dressed up. She had a whole closet full of fancy clothes.

9   Sometimes, Devin talks so **rapidly** that it is hard to understand her. I wish she would speak more slowly.

10   Wild animals do not make good pets. A **tame** animal is much easier to keep in your home.

11   Jacey and Joy used to be friends, but they had a fight, and now they are **enemies**.

12   George has an easy time making friends because he is very **cheerful**. I wish I were as happy as he is.

Synonym/Antonym Cards 1

Name:_____

dull
(use an antonym)

rotten
(use an antonym)

mend
(use a synonym)

silent
(use a synonym)

shallow
(use an antonym)

expensive
(use an antonym)

foolish
(use a synonym)

odd
(use a synonym)

wealthy
(use an antonym)

starving
(use an antonym)

balmy
(use a synonym)

demand
(use a synonym)

gentle
(use an antonym)

seldom
(use an antonym)

boast
(use a synonym)

curved
(use an antonym)

Name:_____

beautiful
(use a synonym)

unusual
(use a synonym)

possible
(use an antonym)

thick
(use an antonym)

scorching
(use a synonym)

fiction
(use a synonym)

firm
(use an antonym)

moist
(use an antonym)

reply
(use a synonym)

anxious
(use a synonym)

different
(use an antonym)

complicated
(use an antonym)

frightened
(use a synonym)

depart
(use a synonym)

inflate
(use an antonym)

rough
(use an antonym)

Directions: Sentence Sort

Whole Class

Discuss synonyms with the class, and explain that there are words that mean the same thing, but to varying degrees. Write the following 12 categories on pieces of paper, and hang them around the room: Hot, Cold, Happy, Angry, Sad, Small, Big, Silly, Scary, Tired, Bad, Good. Reproduce the Sentence Sort pages on pages 42–45, cut them apart, and give a sentence card to every student. Ask students to read the sentences silently, then stand under the heading for which the bold word in the sentence is a synonym. When everyone is in place, have each student read his or her sentence out loud and ask the class to decide if the student is under the correct heading.

Individual/Small Group

Write each category heading on an index card. Then, reproduce the Sentence Sort pages and cut them apart. Place the index cards and the sentences in a learning center. Ask students to sort the sentences into the correct heading categories.

Ask students to discuss the sentences that have words for which they did not know the meaning. Encourage them to identify context clues in the sentences that helped them learn the meaning of the word.

Answer Key

HOT: 1, 23, 32, 40

COLD: 14, 21, 27, 42

HAPPY: 8, 13, 15, 24, 33

ANGRY: 4, 19, 34, 43

SAD: 6, 30, 41, 45, 47

SMALL: 2, 20, 35

BIG: 9, 12, 26, 48

SILLY: 7, 29, 38

SCARY: 11, 17, 18, 36, 44

TIRED: 5, 16, 28, 39

BAD: 10, 31, 37, 46

GOOD: 3, 22, 25

Sentence Sort 1

1 Don't burn your tongue on the soup—it is **boiling**.

2 Maria's baby sister is **tiny** because she was just born.

3 We had a **wonderful** time at the pool, so we want to go back tomorrow.

4 Tory was **furious** because her brother made fun of her.

5 The dog was **exhausted** after his long walk.

6 Are you **unhappy** about moving to a new town and leaving your friends?

7 My Uncle Dan has a **goofy** sense of humor, but I still laugh at his jokes.

8 Most kids are **delighted** when school is out for the summer.

9 The pizza was so **enormous** that we couldn't eat it all.

10 "This apple tastes **awful**," Marshall complained.

11 The movie was so **terrifying** that I had trouble falling asleep last night.

12 Sunflowers can grow to be **gigantic**— some are seven feet tall!

Sentence Sort 2

(13) Rico was **glad** when his dad came home from his trip. He couldn't stop smiling!

(14) We played in the snow for hours, but then we went in because we were **freezing**.

(15) Everyone in class was **merry** because we were having a party later.

(16) The baby is still **drowsy** after her nap, so she might need more sleep.

(17) I read a **frightening** story to my brother, and now he sleeps with the light on.

(18) Hannah knows spiders won't hurt her, but she still thinks they are **creepy**.

(19) Mom gets **irritated** when my sister and I fight in the car.

(20) The dollhouse is filled with **miniature** furniture and tiny people.

(21) "The room feels **icy** to me," Carrie said. "Let's turn on the heater."

(22) Things went **well** on the field trip. Everyone enjoyed themselves.

(23) In summer, the sidewalks are **scorching**. It hurts to walk on them in bare feet.

(24) My report card was very good. My dad was **cheerful** after he looked at it.

(25) The teacher smiled and said I did a **fine** job on my science project.

(26) Jules grew over the summer. Now he felt **huge** compared to the first-graders.

(27) "It's **chilly** today," Dad said. "You need to wear a sweater."

(28) When you have the flu, you will be **weary**, so you should sleep as much as you can.

(29) On **Crazy** Day at school, we always wear the strangest clothes we can find.

(30) Jason was **miserable** when he had to give away his pet turtle.

(31) My little sister thinks spinach tastes **yucky**. She won't eat it!

(32) We raced across the beach because the sand was **baking**. The cool water felt good on our feet.

(33) Jacey was **thrilled** when she opened her birthday present. It was just what she wanted.

(34) Our cat gets **annoyed** when we chase her, so she hides under the bed.

(35) The twins are not the same size. Kelsey is more **petite** than her tall brother.

(36) The monster in the movie was a **spooky** sight.

37 I thought the book was **terrible**.
I had a hard time finishing it.

38 "Now is not the time to be **foolish**," the teacher said. "I want a serious answer."

39 On New Year's Eve, I tried to stay up all night, but I was too **sleepy**.

40 The french fries were **sizzling**, so Desi waited to eat them until they cooled down.

41 I invited 10 friends to my party, but I felt **down** when only five could come.

42 The water in the pool felt **cool** after I sat in the sun.

43 Josie was **frustrated** because her parents wouldn't let her go to the party.

44 "You can't watch that movie by yourself," Mom said. "It is too **spooky**."

45 Our dog always gets **depressed** when we leave her alone all day.

46 Ryan made his mother breakfast, but the eggs tasted **horrible**.

47 Jack was **upset** because his friend Alex was moving away.

48 I had a **giant** milkshake at lunch, and now my stomach hurts.

Directions: Using Picture Clues

Whole Class ●●●

Reproduce What's Wrong with This Picture? 1 or 2 on page 47 or 48 on a transparency. Explain that there is something in each picture that doesn't fit. Have students identify different things in each picture. Ask them if they see anything that doesn't belong. Have students study the picture and write the object that they think doesn't belong on a slip of paper. Have them also write an object they think would be a good replacement for the wrong object. Collect the papers, sort the answers by popularity, and write the results on the board. Ask students to evaluate all the answers: what context clues do they think led to these responses?

Small Group ●●

After students have worked through What's Wrong with This Picture?, provide paper for them to draw their own pictures with wrong objects. Have them include at least three context clues in each picture. When finished, have them swap with their partners. The partner should decide what is wrong in the picture and come up with an alternative object to replace the wrong object.

Individual ●

Reproduce one of the What's Wrong with This Picture? pages for each student. Have students evaluate the pictures to identify the objects that do not belong. Then, have them write their answers and replacement objects below the pictures. They should also circle at least three things in each picture that helped them figure out which object did not belong. Discuss the activity as a class.

Answer Key

What's Wrong with This Picture? 1 (Page 47)

1. milk carton/pot
2. fish/library card
3. sledder/baseball player
4. bear/horse

What's Wrong with This Picture? 2 (Page 48)

1. alligator/briefcase
2. banana/car
3. silverware/fish
4. umbrella/dentist or light

What's Wrong with This Picture? 1

Name:_____

Directions: Find the object that doesn't belong in each picture. Write the object on the lines below. Then write what should actually be in the picture.

What's Wrong with This Picture? 2

Name:_____

Directions: Find the object that doesn't belong in each picture. Write the object on the lines below. Then write what should actually be in the picture.